**Cherril Prentice**

Dirty Dilbert the Smelly Gnome

Nightingale Books

NIGHTINGALE PAPERBACK

A CIP catalogue record for this title is
available from the British Library.
ISBN 978-1-83875-522-5

Nightingale Books is an imprint of
Pegasus Elliot MacKenzie Publishers Ltd.
www.pegasuspublishers.com

First Published in 2023

Nightingale Books
Sheraton House  Castle Park
Cambridge  England

Printed & Bound in Great Britain

**Dedication**

I dedicate this book to my grandchildren,

Polly Budworth, Johnny Budworth and

Lola Budworth with loads of love.

In the middle of a deep, dark wood, that folk have never seen,

There is a glade that's beautiful, with flowers, ferns and stream.

It's where the fairy folk all live, that humans cannot see,

They live in peace and harmony, it's where they love to be.

At one old tree, within that wood, you'd need to hold your nose,

It's the home of smelly Dilbert, who has beetles in his toes.

He really is a dirty gnome, a bath he's never had,

His clothes and hair are filthy, the smell is very bad.

His breath is really horrid; his teeth should not be seen,

He hasn't got that many, and what he has are almost green!

He has a very bogey nose, his eyes are very starey,

His hair, like string, hangs down his back, his chest is very hairy.

If you got close, you'd see his bugs, though I don't think that you should,

He really is quite dreadful, is Dilbert from the wood.

There is another gnome nearby and they get on quite well,

They call him happy Horace and he has no sense of smell.

He got on well within the wood, where he liked to be seen,

And he was very tidy and scrupulously clean!

His face was washed, his hair was combed, his clothes were clean and bright,

You'd hear him singing in his bath, which he had every night.

Now every week these two old gnomes would sit and have a talk

And, if they had the energy, they'd even take a walk.

As they strolled through the pretty glade, the fairy folk would laugh

And say, "Eh Horace, can't you make old Dilbert take a bath?"

The two old gnomes would walk on past,
the comments they ignored,

But it started to peeve Horace, but
Dilbert just got bored.

One day, whilst sitting by the stream,
Horace asked Dilbert, why

He never washed or combed his hair and
Dilbert gave a sigh.

He said, "Why Horace, what's the point,
when I live all alone?"

But this annoyed old Horace, and he let
out a groan.

He lost his temper, just this once, and he
began to shout,

"That's your own fault, you stinky man",
that left him in no doubt!

Horace got up and strode away, he started to feel bad,

He should have kept his temper, and he felt very sad.

Dilbert then sat upon a bench and wriggled his filthy toes,

He scratched his chest and gave a belch, then picked his bogey nose.

A thought then came across his mind, that sort of made him think,

He wondered, should he have a bath and get rid of this stink?

It worried him that Horace had really got so mad,

He was old Dilbert's buddy, the only one he had.

That night, old Dilbert lay in bed,
surrounded by his stink,

He couldn't get to sleep, you see, he really
had to think.

It was then that he decided that
something must be done

The thought made him quite horrified, it
wouldn't be much fun.

Before the fairy folk awoke, Dilbert went
to the stream,

Had he really thought this through or was
it just a dream?

The thought that he should have a bath
was really very queer

He'd never had this thought before, and
he was filled with fear.

What if he didn't like it, his eyes crossed
in a frown,

What if he slipped whilst in there, was it
deep enough to drown?

But then he thought of Horace, and how
happy he would be,

He'd put one foot in, first of all, and have
a little see.

The beetles were just horrified, this thing
they'd never seen

Old Dilbert, with his foot about to go right
in the stream.

In one quick rush they all flew off and
Dilbert fell, headfirst,

He let out such a piercing scream, you'd
think his lungs would burst.

As sun arose, the fairy folk awoke to such a din

Then someone shouted out with glee, "Old Dilbert just fell in".

They all went to the little stream, this spectacle to see

And they expected Dilbert to be as mad as mad could be.

Instead of this, the sight they saw just made them stand and stare

Old Dilbert, splashing, laughing and washing bugs out of his hair.

"Well, who'd have thought it, what a sight?" laughed Horace with delight,

And all the fairy folk joined in at this unexpected sight.

They got their heads together and after
giving it much thought

Decided to clean Dilbert's home, so magic
must be sort.

They didn't get too close because the
smell was really bad

So, wands outstretched and noses held,
they cleaned and cleaned like mad.

Now very soon the house was clean, but
what would Dilbert think?

Would he like his nice clean home or
prefer the dirty stink?

They looked around for Dilbert, where was
that little gnome?

They had to find out what he thought of his
bright clean, shiny home.

He was still splashing in the stream and
giggling with glee,

A happier little gnome they knew they'd
never ever see.

Eventually they persuaded him to get out
of the stream

And then told him about his home now that
it was nice and clean.

He didn't seem too happy but agreed to
go and see

This lovely, sweetly smelling home in his old
gnarly tree.

He gave a great big whoop of joy and with
a rueful look

Realised how hard it must have been to
live beside such muck.

He promised them that from now on he'd
keep it nice and clean

And bath each day and wash his clothes
and stop being so mean.

If you should walk on through that glade,
with all its magic powers

The only thing that you would smell would
be the lovely scent of flowers.

So when you're told to have a bath, don't
grumble and get mad

Or you'll end up like Dilbert was, alone,
smelly and sad.

## About the Author

I am a wife, mother of two sons, a grandmother to three beautiful grandchildren and have two golden doodle dogs. I spent my working life as a secretary and in my spare time enjoyed amateur dramatics and singing. Now, in my retirement, I am lucky to live part of my life on the west of the Isle of Wight and the rest at my home in Swadlincote, South Derbyshire. For a few years I have enjoyed writing rhymes, usually very short, silly ones and that's how Philomena, my first book, came to be.

## Acknowledgements

Acknowledgements to my husband Malcolm, who encouraged me to write this second book and also to Mary Brearley who bought me a new notebook and told me to get writing.